F[...]

This primer booklet on Fibonacci numbers is intended to:

1. Give the reader an initial acquaintance with the concepts of the Fibonacci number sequence,

2. To provide historical background,

3. To give an idea of how Fibonacci concepts and ratios are used by stock and commodity traders and analysts, and

4. To provide a comprehensive bibliography and list of informational sources, with accompanying comments on the ones I consider most worthwhile for the Fibonacci student interested in applying the concepts to trading stocks and commodities.

This booklet is not intended to give complete and comprehensive coverage to this fascinating subject. This would be impossible in such a limited space. The primary emphasis is not on the profound influence Fibonacci has had in art, architecture, geometry, mathematics, and other areas, but on how the trader of stocks and commodities can put this information to practical use.

I am grateful to my friend, Robert Prechter, one of the most knowledgeable "Fibonacci disciples" I know, for his permission to borrow from his thought and work in composing this booklet.

Edward Dobson

Edward D. Dobson, President   September, 1984
Traders Press, Inc.®
Greenville, S.C.

ISBN: 0-934380-08-2

Published by Traders Press, Inc.®

**Traders Press, Inc.®
PO Box 6206
Greenville, SC 29606**

Serving Traders since 1975

800-927-8222 ~ 864-298-0222 ~ Fax 864-298-0221
e-mail ~ **customerservice@traderspress.com**
Website ~ **http://www.traderspress.com**

OVERVIEW

The most important mathematician of the Middle Ages was Leonardo Fibonacci da Pisa, born in Pisa, Italy around 1170. It is reported that after a sabbatical to the Middle East, Fibonacci returned from Egypt with a mysterious set of numbers, which now bear his name. Fibonacci discovered many remarkable properties of these numbers. While in Egypt, he studied at length the Great Pyramid of Gizeh, and noticed that the ancient Egyptians had, consciously or not, integrated the "Golden Ratio" into the geometrical proportions of the pyramid.

THE FIBONACCI NUMBERS

The Fibonacci sequence of numbers begins with 1,1 and progresses to infinity with each successive number in the sequence derived by ADDING the two previous numbers.

The sequence: 1, 1, 2, 3, 5, 8, 13, 21, 34, 55, 89, 144, 233, 377, 610, etc., to infinity.

PROPERTIES OF THE FIBONACCI NUMBERS

After the first four numbers in the sequence, examination will reveal the following relationships between these numbers:

(1) The sum of any two adjacent numbers gives the next higher number in the sequence.

(2) Any given number approximates 1.618 times the number preceding it. The higher the number, the closer it approaches this ratio.

(3) Any given number approximates .618 of the number following. The higher the number, the closer it approaches this ratio.

(4) Between alternate numbers, the SECOND HIGHER number approximates 2.618 times the first number (E.g., 233 versus 89).

(5) Between alternate numbers, the second number down has the ratio of .382 (the inverse of 2.618) to the first number (E.g., 55 versus 144).

Further properties of the Fibonacci numbers are discussed in Prechter's ELLIOTT WAVE PRINCIPLE, and are reprinted below from that work:

Thus the ratio of any number to the next higher, called phi, is approximately .618 to 1 and to the next lower number approximately 1.618 to 1. The higher the numbers, the closer to .618 and 1.618 are the ratios between the numbers. Between alternate numbers in the sequence, the ratio is 2.618, or its inverse, .382. Some statements of the interrelated properties of these four main ratios can be listed as follows:

1) $2.618 - 1.618 = 1.$
2) $1.618 - .618 = 1.$
3) $1 - .618 = .382.$
4) $2.618 \times .382 = 1.$
5) $2.618 \times .618 = 1.618.$
6) $1.618 \times .618 = 1.$
7) $.618 \times .618 = .382.$
8) $1.618 \times 1.618 = 2.618.$

Besides 1 and 2, any Fibonacci number multiplied by four, when added to a selected Fibonacci number, gives another Fibonacci number, so that:

$$3 \times 4 = 12; \quad + 1 = 13.$$
$$5 \times 4 = 20; \quad + 1 = 21.$$
$$8 \times 4 = 32; \quad + 2 = 34.$$
$$13 \times 4 = 52; \quad + 3 = 55.$$
$$21 \times 4 = 84; \quad + 5 = 89, \text{ and so on.}$$

As the new sequence progresses, a third sequence is begun in those numbers that are added to the 4x multiple. This relationship is possible because the ratio between _second_ alternate Fibonacci numbers is 4.236, where .236 is both its inverse _and_ its difference from the number 4. This continuous series-building property is reflected at other multiples for the same reasons.

We offer a partial list of additional phenomena relating to the Fibonacci sequence as follows:

1) If we list the Fibonacci sequence and count forward, labeling each Fibonacci number 1, 2, 3, 4, 5, 6, 7, etc., we find that each time a prime number (one divisible only by itself and 1) label is reached, we have a prime Fibonacci number listed in the sequence.

2) Next, we find that, except for the fourth Fibonacci number (3), all composite numbers (those divisible by at least two numbers besides themselves and 1) label composite Fibonacci sequence numbers, as in the table below.

Fibonacci: Prime vs. Composite

P	P	P	X	P	C	P	C	C	C	P	C	P	C	C	C
1	2	3	4	5	6	7	8	9	10	11	12	13	14	15	16
1	1	2	3	5	8	13	21	34	55	89	144	233	377	610	987

3) The sum of any ten numbers in the sequence is divisible by 11.

4) No two consecutive Fibonacci numbers have any common factors.

5) The sum of all Fibonacci numbers in the sequence up to any point, plus 1, equals the Fibonacci number two steps ahead of the last one added.

6) The sum of the squares of any consecutive sequence of Fibonacci numbers beginning at the first 1 will always equal the last number of the sequence chosen times the next higher number.

7) The square of a Fibonacci number minus the square of the second number below it in the sequence is always a Fibonacci number.

8) The square of any Fibonacci number is equal to the number before it in the sequence multiplied by the number after it in the sequence plus or minus 1. The plus and minus 1 alternate along the sequence.

9) One mind-stretching phenomenon, which to our knowledge has not previously been mentioned, is that the ratios between Fibonacci numbers yield numbers which very nearly are thousandths of other Fibonacci numbers with the difference being a thousandth of a third Fibonacci number, all in sequence (see ratio table, Figure 63). Thus, in ascending direction, identical Fibonacci numbers are related by 1.00, or .987 plus .013, adjacent Fibonacci numbers are related by 1.618, or 1.597 plus .021, alternate Fibonacci numbers are related by 2.618, or 2.464 plus .034, and so on. In the descending direction, adjacent Fibonacci numbers are related by .618, or .610 plus .008; alternate Fibonacci numbers are related by .382, or .377 plus .005; second alternates are related by .236, or .233 plus .003; third alternates are related by .146, or .144 plus .002; fourth alternates are related by .090, or .089 plus .001; fifth alternates are related by .056, or .055 plus .001; sixth through twelfth alternates are related by ratios which are themselves thousandths of Fibonacci numbers beginning with .034. It is interesting that by this analysis, the ratio then between thirteenth alternate Fibonacci numbers begins the series back at .001, one thousandth of where it began! On all counts, we have truly a creation of "like from like," of "reproduction in an endless series."

Finally, we note that $(\sqrt{5} + 1)/2 = 1.618$ and $(\sqrt{5} - 1)/2 = .618$, where $\sqrt{5} = 2.236$, an important factor in the Wave Principle and the logarithmic spiral.

Some further properties of the Fibonacci sequence are found in Beckman's SUPERTIMING, on pages 54-56. For the die-hard mathematician, the most exhaustive and "mind-boggling" study of the numbers I have seen is the book FIBONACCI NUMBERS, by the Russian mathematician, N. N. Vorobev.

FIBONACCI-RELATED TERMS

THE GOLDEN RATIO (OR GOLDEN MEAN): The ratios of 1.618 to 1 or .618 to 1.

THE GOLDEN SECTION: Any length can be divided in such a way that the ratio between the smaller part and the larger part is equivalent to the ratio between the larger part and the whole. That ratio is always .618 to 1.

THE GOLDEN RECTANGLE: One whose sides are in the proportion of 1.618 to 1. The proportions of this booklet approximate those of a golden rectangle.

THE GOLDEN (LOGARITHMIC) SPIRAL: A shape conforming to the Fibonacci relationships often found in nature, as in the snail's shell and in the spiral galaxies of outer space. See discussion in Prechter's ELLIOTT WAVE PRINCIPLE, pages 86-97.

PHI (ϕ): A letter in the Greek alphabet which refers to the ratio of any number to the next higher (.618 to 1) and to the next lower (1.618 to 1).

WHERE ARE FIBONACCI RELATIONSHIPS FOUND?

We find the influence of Fibonacci relationships, and the incidence of Fibonacci numbers, throughout the fields of art, architecture, geometry, mathematics, in the financial markets, and even in nature itself. As previously mentioned, the ancient Egyptians constructed the pyramids in a way that embodies the Fibonacci proportions. The Greeks, who called the .618 to 1 ratio the "GOLDEN MEAN", made this proportion an integral part of their art and architecture. Leonardo da Vinci used this proportion in his art. This ratio is an integral part of musical harmony. There is a continual occurrence of Fibonacci numbers and the golden spiral in nature, e.g. in sunflowers, the shell of the snail, even the vast spiral galaxies of outer space. Of greatest interest and significance to you as a trader is the fact that the Fibonacci numbers and relationships appear repeatedly and with a high degree of consistency in market price action.

FIBONACCI IN THE FINANCIAL MARKETS

The study of how Fibonacci numbers and relationships manifest themselves in the price action of markets is inextricably interwoven with the tenets and principles of the Elliott Wave Principle. It is through a study and understanding of Elliott Wave Theory that one reaches an understanding of the interaction of Fibonacci and the financial markets. R. N. Elliott tells us that the Fibonacci sequence is the mathematical basis for the Elliott Wave Principle.

There are three primary aspects of stock and commodity price behavior:

PATTERN, TIME and RATIO. Each of these can be shown to be a predictable function of the Fibonacci progression.

The PATTERN of market behavior relates to the price waves or movements. Elliott Wave analysis postulates that bull moves consist of 3 primary and 2 corrective waves, a total of 5...all Fibonacci numbers. Bear moves have two waves down and one corrective wave, a total of 3. A complete cycle comprised of both a bull and bear move

involves 8 major waves. When these major waves are broken down and
studied in greater detail, each of the 3 major upward waves in a bull
move consists, in turn, of smaller intermediate waves, 3 upward and 2
corrective, and each of the major down waves consists of 3
intermediate waves, 2 down and 1 corrective. Elliott states in
Nature's Law: "In a complete cycle of the stock market, the number of
minor waves is 144. Bull markets usually have 5 major waves, in turn
consisting of 21 intermediate waves, and 89 minor waves. Bear markets
consist of 3 major waves, in turn subdivided into 13 intermediate and
55 minor waves. Thus in a complete cycle, the total number of waves is
as follows: Major 8, intermediate 34, and minor 144. All are Fibonacci
numbers and the entire series is employed. The length of waves may
vary, but not the number."

  Another aspect of market behavior where the application of
Fibonacci numbers can be helpful in forecasting is TIME. The duration
of price movements in a given direction can be shown to bear a close
relationship to Fibonacci numbers. For example, there might be 34 or
55 months between a major high and low, or 13 or 21 days between minor
highs and lows. Some analysts carry this concept to the area of
day-trading, as described by Angell in his HOW TO TRIPLE YOUR MONEY IN
STOCK INDEX FUTURES. Tucker Emmett's article, described later, is
excellent in providing examples of this phenomenon, as well as the
next.

  The final aspect of market behavior to which the Fibonacci
sequence applies is RATIO, the proportionate relationship of one
price wave to another, both in time and in amplitude. This aspect of
Fibonacci analysis also involves the analysis of percentage
retracements of a given price move, with the observation that many
retracements will correct 38.2% or 61.8% or the preceding price move.
I am personally especially interested in this particular aspect of the
theory, as it relates so closely to the concepts with which I deal in
my own book, THE TRADING RULE THAT CAN MAKE YOU RICH*.

  Tucker Emmett, in his excellent article FIBONACCI CYCLES AND
COMMODITY PRICE BEHAVIOR, gives an interesting description and summary
of the three factors mentioned above:

  "Briefly, our basic thesis is as follows. The actions of men
and events appear to follow cyclical rhythms and patterns...all
seeming to occur at specified time intervals. These time intervals
seem to be accurately and adequately described by reference to the
mathematical series discovered by Fibonacci...
  Elliott seized upon this series and applied it to variations in
prices seen in the stock market, reasoning that these should follow
the same form of cyclical patterns as man's other actions do. By very
careful application, he was able to ascertain to his own satisfaction
that ...... there are 89 minor waves in a bull market and 55 minor
waves in a bear market (both Fibonacci numbers). He also ascertained
that the length of time involved in the completion of a bull move or a
bear move was a Fibonacci number (13 weeks for instance, or 21 days in
another case), and further propounded that the distance a bull move or
a bear move carries is a Fibonacci ratio (.618, 1.618, or 2.618) in
relationship to the previous bull or bear move.
  Sound pretty complicated? Not really. Our basic thesis is that
stock prices and commodity prices follow PATTERN, TIME, AND RATIO, and
that each of these is a predictable function of the Fibonacci
progression."

   EXAMPLE OF FIBONACCI MARKET ANALYSIS

  I am grateful to FUTURES MAGAZINE, 219 Parkade, Cedar Falls,
IA 50613 for permission to reprint the following article by Robert
Prechter, which appeared in the August, 1982 issue. This was the most
effective and concise means I could find to convey an overview of the
application of Fibonacci analysis to market action.

Does Fibonacci rule the stock indexes?

By Robert R. Prechter Jr.

For anyone trying to discover mathematical relationships in markets, the Elliott Wave Principle can satisfy even the most cynical researcher.

A side element of the Wave Principle is evidence that the Fibonacci ratio expresses itself often enough in the averages to make it clear that it is indeed a governing force — not necessarily *the* governing force — on stock market indexes.

The Fibonacci ratio is so compelling because the 1.618:1 ratio is the only price relationship whereby the length of the shorter wave under consideration is to the length of the longer wave as the length of the longer wave is to the length of the entire distance traveled, thus creating an interlocking wholeness to the price structure. It was this property that led early mathematicians to dub 1.618:1 as the "Golden Ratio."

Anticipating ratios

In a nutshell, the portion of the theory which applies to anticipating the occurrence of Fibonacci ratios in the market can be stated this way:

1. The Wave Principle describes the movement of markets.
2. The numbers of waves in each degree of trend correspond to the Fibonacci sequence.
3. The Fibonacci ratio is the governor of the Fibonacci sequence.
4. The Fibonacci ratio has reason to be evident in the market.

R.N. Elliott discovered that a Fibonacci relationship between adjacent waves occurs more often within corrective patterns. A Fibonacci relationship between unconnected waves that are nevertheless part of a single pattern occurs more often within five

wave sequences when the third wave is the longest. Price relationships are calculated only with reference to vertical points traveled.

Others have pointed out, sometimes in advance for forecasting purposes, the 1.618 relationships found in the following time periods:

• 1921-28 — the final wave (1926-28) of the sequence is 1.618 times as long as the first three (1921-1925).

• 1932-37 — the final wave (1934-37) is 1.618 times as long as the first three (1932-33).

• 1930-39 — each of four swings is related to the ensuing swing by 1.618.

• 1949-66 — the last decade (1957-66) is 1.618 times 1949-56.

• 1966-74 — the distance from 1966 to 1974 is 1.618 times the length of the 1966 decline.

The period from 1974 to the present has been less documented but deserves mention for the frequent occurrence of the 1.618 ratio during this period. All Fibonacci relationships in all the interlocking waves during this time span could not possibly be mentioned here, but a few of the most striking can serve to illustrate the influence.

Aug. 12, 1980 — Dec. 11, 1980 (fig. 1)

This sideways pattern began from the point at which the orthodox top of five waves from April 21 to Aug. 12, 1980, ended. (An "orthodox" turning point is one which marks the end of an Elliott Wave pattern, ensuing minor new highs or lows notwithstanding.)

The height of each A-B-C pattern in this sequence is related to the preceding A-B-C pattern by 1.618 (with 1% error and 6% error respectively). The height of the final A-B-C pattern is

2.618 times the height of the first.

If the December low (899.57) had been 905.84, the second calculation would have had 0% error. If we label the first pattern "X", the second "Y" and the third "Z", note that X:Y as Y:Z; X:Y as Y:(X + Y); Y:Z as Z:(Y + Z). The whole pattern is an interlocking expression of the Fibonacci ratio.

Dec. 11, 1980 — Dec. 4, 1981 (fig. 2)

The April-September decline is 1.618 times the December-April advance (4% error), and the December-April advance is 1.618 times the September-December advance (3% error). The April-September decline is 2.618 times the September-December advance (1% error). These would have had 0% error if both the December 1980 low (899.57) and the December 1981 high (893.55) had been 894.37.

In other words, the entire height of the pattern in divided into a Golden Section at 894. If we label these lengths P, Q and R, you can see that R:P as P:Q; R:P as P:(R + P); P:Q as Q:(P + Q). On the chart, a rectangle can encompass all this price action, which is divided into the Golden Section proportion at its exact beginning and end.

1974-82 (fig. 3)

Now we come to the most interesting pattern, the big picture from 1974. Each wave since 1974 is related to an adjacent wave by 1.618 (or in the center of the pattern by equality), within the percentage errors as listed. The only large deviation is the "overshoot" in the October 1978 massacre. During the October-December 1978 period, the first ideal retracement level at 806 was penetrated eight times in whipsaw action. All of these

**Triple three —
Aug.-Dec. 1980**

2nd ABC = 1.618 × 1st ABC (1% error)
3rd ABC = 1.618 × 2nd ABC (6% error)
3rd ABC = 2.618 × 1st ABC (5% error)

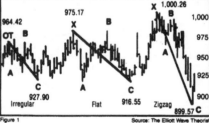

Figure 1

Source: The Elliott Wave Theorist

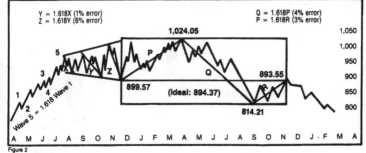

Y = 1.618X (1% error)
Z = 1.618Y (6% error)
Q = 1.618P (4% error)
P = 1.618R (3% error)

1,024.05

899.57   (Ideal: 894.37)

893.55

814.21

With division at 894.37, all calculations have 0% error. December 1980 low at 899.57 is a compromise between an ideal 905.84 for the XYZ pattern and an ideal 894.37 for the PQR pattern.

Dow-Jones Average of 30 Industrials

Figure 2

penetrations were extremely volatile, so much so that five of them left intra-day gaps in the Dow.

Among the three that did not leave gaps were a 9-point "up" opening hour and a 17-point "down" opening hour. That kind of action may indicate that the market sensed the importance of the exact Fibonacci retracement level despite the overshoot. The next largest deviation occurred because of the mild overshoot at the November 1979 low, which was again due to a "massacre" type market.

1974-82 (fig. 4)

A second way of looking at this period is to average the tops in 1976, producing 1,013.08, and the tops in 1980-81, producing 1,011.51. It so happens that a rounded average of the two, which gives a central peak point of 1,012, is the exact point which provides 0% error for the Fibonacci relationships involved.

Similarly, the average of the tops in 1978-80 is 908 and the average of the bottoms in 1978-79 is 789. The three average price points make all the Fibonacci ratio relationships perfect except for the average of the 1978-79 bottoms, which is 15 points below the ideal low of 804. However, 789 has its own particular "raison d'etre."

Solid support

So far this year, the 789 level has acted as solid support for the Dow-Jones Industrial Average. It marked the exact hourly low in March and the hourly low so far in June.

This same support point has stopped cold three declines since 1974. Why? The 792 level just happens to fall right at the halfway (50%) level of the entire pattern back to the 1974 low. Perhaps

Robert R. Prechter Jr. is editor of The Elliott Wave Theorist *financial letter, Gainesville, Ga.*

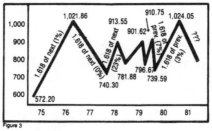

Hourly turning points ( ) indicates deviation from ideal length

The Fibonacci Ratio in the Dow from 1974

Figure 3

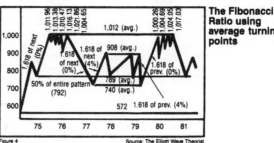

The Fibonacci Ratio using average turning points

Figure 4   Source: The Elliott Wave Theorist

this explains why the two bottoms in 1978 and 1979 were off a bit from their ideal Fibonacci target at 804 and gravitated to 789.

789 also happens to be the level at which the decline from the peak in December 1981 would be 1.618 times the length of the April-May decline. These two declines can be labeled as fifth and first waves respectively. To see another example of this type of relationship, see the 1980 five-wave advance in fig. 2, where wave 5 = 1.618 × wave 1.

With reference to fig. 3, I've calculated that if the down wave which began in 1981 were to fall 1.618 times the length of the preceding advance, it would bottom at 563.79 and create a symmetrical pattern from 1974. That

level should not be taken as a forecast at this point but would certainly become likely if 789 is broken on the downside any time this year. On the other hand, if 789 holds, another new bull market could well get underway.

Does the Fibonacci ratio govern every move in every market, as some analysts suggest? Definitely not. My studies show that there are many times when one should not expect a Fibonacci relationship. Knowing when to look for one is the key to successful application, and I haven't found any exceptions to Elliott's discoveries in that regard.

No, old Fibonacci doesn't rule the world. But if he were a trader, he might well own the New York Stock Exchange.   □

For those who find Mr. Prechter's analysis of interest, I would suggest writing him, c/o New Classics Library, P.O. Box 1618, Gainesville, GA 30503 and requesting information on his excellent publication and service, THE ELLIOTT WAVE THEORIST.

WHY DOES FIBONACCI ANALYSIS WORK?

There are a number of highly useful technical tools, many of which relate to recurrent patterns of market behavior. It is very difficult, perhaps impossible, to explain why these patterns and phenomena recur. Nevertheless, I personally place far more faith in the recurrence of certain of these market habits (see my book, THE TRADING RULE THAT CAN MAKE YOU RICH*) than I do in the most exacting and precise fundamental analysis performed by the most knowledgeable and capable analysts in the world! And it matters not one whit that we really can't adequately explain WHY they continue to recur and to "work."

Again to quote Elliott:

"Even though we may not understand the cause underlying a particular phenomenon, we can, by observation, predict the phenomenon's recurrence."

COMMENTS ON FIBONACCI REFERENCES

The bibliography of Fibonacci references which follows gives a number of excellent source materials on the various aspects of Fibonacci. If you are a serious student of the market (as I feel one MUST be, in order to survive as a successful trader in the long run), you will undoubtedly want to add some of these titles to your library. Most of these works are available through TRADERS PRESS, INC., P.O. Box 6206, Greenville, SC 29606. Please write for a list of the titles which are available, their cost, and a brief description of each. The comments which follow pertain to the titles which I especially recommend.

Angell: HOW TO TRIPLE YOUR MONEY IN STOCK INDEX FUTURES. Chapter 6 contains some interesting applications of the use of Fibonacci numbers in day-trading. Angell's "Golden Rule" states that ". . . you should look for a retracement in prices of .618 times the initial move."

DiNapoli: Joe DiNapoli's FIBONACCI MONEY MANAGEMENT AND TREND ANALYSIS TRADING COURSE. For those who want to know all there is to know about the practical application of Fibonacci technqiues and principles to trading. Written and produced by the leading expert on and proponent of Fibonacci-related trading principles. Available through Traders Press.

Dobson: THE TRADING RULE THAT CAN MAKE YOU RICH*. Although this book does not deal with Fibonacci directly, it does deal with a similar concept, that is, a recurrent pattern of market behavior, which when recognized by the trained eye, becomes a highly effective and easily utilized trading tool. In nearly 20 years of trading, this is the simplest, yet the most useful technique that I have encountered.

Eng: TECHNICAL ANALYSIS OF STOCKS, OPTIONS, AND FUTURES: ADVANCED TRADING SYSTEMS AND TECHNIQUES. This excellent book takes 15 major trading techniques and gives major coverage to each, including an evaluation of how well each works in varying market conditions and situations. The section on the use of Fibonacci numbers in trading is especially helpful in showing the trader how to apply Fibonacci cycles.

Kaufman: COMMODITY TRADING SYSTEMS AND METHODS. Though the Fibonacci coverage in this book is brief (about seven pages), it contains unique ideas and analysis not found elsewhere; for example, the use of Lucas numbers in conjunction with Fibonacci numbers to further enhance their effectiveness. In many ways, this is one of the most valuable books in print for the technical analyst. EVERY technical trader should own this book.

Murphy: TECHNICAL ANALYSIS OF THE FUTURES MARKETS. Extremely comprehensive, well-written, superlative book. Pages 394-398 cover principles of Fibonacci numbers, the logarithmic spiral, Fibonacci ratios and retracements, Fibonacci time targets, and Fibonacci numbers in the study of cycles. Pages 408-412 cover Fibonacci fan lines, arcs, and time zones.

Prechter: ELLIOTT WAVE THEORY. This is one book I would consider indispensable on the subject and was the single best reference I was able to locate on Fibonacci.

RJV Financial Services: TRADING WITH FIBONACCI WAVE PROJECTIONS. Practical and easy to use Fibonacci projection technique. Teaches you how to construct and "confirm a Fibonacci Wave projection by using a simple worksheet approach."

BIBLIOGRAPHY: FIBONACCI REFERENCES

Adler, Irving. THE GIANT GOLDEN BOOK OF MATHEMATICS. New York: Golden Press, 1960.

Angell, George. TRIPLE YOUR MONEY EVERY YEAR WITH STOCK INDEX FUTURES.

Asimov, Isaac. ASIMOV ON NUMBERS. New York: Doubleday & Co., 1977.

Balzer, Horst. NATURAL LOGARITHM.

Basin, S.L. "The Fibonacci Sequence As It Appears In Nature." FIBONACCI QUARTERLY 1 (February 1963): 53-64.

Beckman, Robert C. SUPERTIMING: THE UNIQUE ELLIOTT WAVE SYSTEM.

Beerbower, James R. A SEARCH FOR THE PAST. Englewood Cliffs, NJ: Prentice-Hall, 1960.

Benjafield, J., and J. Adams-Webber. "The Golden Section Hypothesis." BRITISH JOURNAL OF PSYCHOLOGY 67, no. 1 (1976): 11-15.

Brousseau, Br. U. Alfred. AN INTRODUCTION TO FIBONACCI DISCOVERY. San Jose, CA: San Jose State University, The Fibonacci Association, 1965.

Cook, Theodore Andrea. THE CURVES OF LIFE. New York: Dover Publications, 1979.

Coxeter, H.S.M. INTRODUCTION TO GEOMETRY. New York: Dover Publications, 1979.

Davis, T. Anthony, and Rudolf Altevogt. "Golden Mean of the Human Body." FIBONACCI QUARTERLY 17 (December 1979): 340-44.

Deininger, Rolf. "Fibonacci Numbers and Water Pollution Control." FIBONACCI QUARTERLY 10 (April 1972): 299-302.

DiNapoli, Joe. FIBONACCI MONEY MANAGEMENT AND TREND ANALYSIS TRADING COURSE.

Dobson, Edward. UNDERSTANDING FIBONACCI NUMBERS. Greenville, SC. Traders Press, Inc., 1984.

Duffy, Joe. TIME POINTS: ANALYSIS TECHNIQUES FOR PREDICTING HIGH, LOW AND TREND CHANGE DATES. "Fibonacci Based Trend Change Points."

Emmett, Tucker J. FIBONACCI CYCLES AND COMMODITY PRICE BEHAVIOR.

Eng, William. TECHNICAL ANALYSIS OF STOCKS, OPTIONS AND FUTURES: ADVANCED TRADING SYSTEMS AND TECHNIQUES. Chapter 15, Fibonacci Numbers: Cycles Which Build On The Past. Pages 403-416.

Eves, Howard W. "The Fibonacci Numbers." TIME, 4 April 1969.

Faulconbridge, Albert J. FIBONACCI SUMMATION ECONOMICS PART I. The Fibonacci Quarterly: The Official Journal of the Fibonacci Association 2, no. 4, (December 1964): 320-22.

Faulconbridge, Albert J. FIBONACCI SUMMATION ECONOMICS PART II. The Fibonacci Quarterly: The Official Journal of the Fibonacci Association 3, no. 4, (December 1965): 309-14.

FIBONNACI QUARTERLY. Published by The Fibonacci Association, Santa Clara University, Santa Clara, CA, 1963-1986.

Fischer, Kurt. "The Fibonacci Sequence Encountered in Nerve Physiology." FIBONACCI QUARTERLY 14 (November 1976): 377-79.

Fischer, Robert. THE GOLDEN SECTION COMPASS.

Gardner, Helen. ART THROUGH THE AGES. New York: Harcourt Brace Jovanovich, 1980.

Gardner, Martin. "A Discussion of Helical Structures, from Corkscrews to DNA Molecules." SCIENTIFIC AMERICAN, June 1963.

_____. MATHEMATICAL CIRCUS. New York: Alfred A. Knopf, 1979.

_____. MATHEMATICS, MAGIC AND MYSTERY. New York: Dover Publications, 1956.

_____. "The Multiple Fascination of the Fibonacci Sequence."
SCIENTIFIC AMERICAN, March 1969.

_____. THE 2nd SCIENTIFIC AMERICAN BOOK OF MATHEMATICAL PUZZLES
AND DIVERSIONS. New York: Simon and Schuster, 1961.

Garland, Trudi Hammel. FASCINATING FIBONACCIS: MYSTERY AND MAGIC IN
NUMBERS.

Garrett, William C. INVESTING FOR PROFIT WITH TORQUE ANALYSIS OF
STOCK MARKET CYCLES. Pages 84-95.

Gettings, Fred. THE MEANING AND WONDER OF ART. New York: Golden
Press, 1963.

Ghyka, Matila. THE GEOMETRY OF ART AND LIFE.

Gies, Joseph and Francis. LEONARD OF PISA AND THE MATHEMATICS OF THE
MIDDLE AGES.

GOLDEN SECTION. Wilmette, IL: Films, Inc., Macmillan Films, 1968.
(Film)

Hambridge, Jay. THE ELEMENTS OF DYNAMIC SYMMETRY.

Hamon, J.D. ADVANCED COMMODITY TRADING TECHNIQUES. Chapter 2: Winning
With Fibonacci. Pages 23-32.

Hamon, J.D. BREAKTHROUGHS IN COMMODITY TECHNICAL ANALYSIS. Chapter 6,
"Fast Fib Analysis." Pages 91-118. Windsor Books, 1985.

Hedian, Helene. "The Golden Section and the Artist." FIBONACCI QUAR-
TERLY 14 (December 1976): 406-18.

Hoffer, Alan. MATHEMATICS IN NATURE POSTERS. Palo Alto, CA: Creative
Publications, 1978.

Hoffer, Williams. "A Magic Ratio Occurs Throughout Art and Nature."
SMITHSONIAN, December 1975.

Hoggatt, Verner E. "Number Theory: The Fibonacci Sequence." In 1977
YEARBOOK OF SCIENCE AND THE FUTURE. Chicago: Encyclopedia
Britannica, 1976.

_____. FIBONACCI AND LUCAS NUMBERS. Boston: Houghton Mifflin, 1969.

Horadam, A.F. "Further Appearance of the Fibonacci Sequence." FIBON-
ACCI QUARTERLY 1 (December 1963): 41-46.

Huntley, H.E. THE DIVINE PROPORTION: A STUDY IN MATHEMATICAL BEAUTY.

Jacobs, Harold R. MATHEMATICS, A HUMAN ENDEAVOR. San Francisco: W.H.
Freeman, 1970.

Kaufman, Perry. COMMODITY TRADING SYSTEMS AND METHODS. Pages 192-197.

King, Charles. "Leonardo Fibonacci." FIBONACCI QUARTERLY 1 (December 1963): 15-19.

Larson, Paul. "The Golden Section in the Earliest Notated Western Music." FIBONACCI QUARTERLY 9 (December 1978): 513-15.

Lowman, Edward A. "Some Striking Proportions in the Music of Bela Bartok." FIBONACCI QUARTERLY 9 (December 1971): 527-37.

Meyer, Jerome. FUN WITH MATHEMATICS. New York: World Publishing Co., 1952.

Murphy, John J. TECHNICAL ANALYSIS OF THE FUTURES MARKETS. Pages 394-398 (principles), and pages 408-412 (applications).

O'Connor, William. STOCK, WHEAT, AND PHAROAHS.

Plank, Charles. PLANK'S GOLDEN RATIO SYSTEM. PLANK'S GOLDEN SECTION CHANGE IN TREND LOCATOR SYSTEM.

Prechter, Robert. THE MAJOR WORKS OF R.N. ELLIOTT.

Prechter, Robert. THE ELLIOTT WAVE PRINCIPLE.

Ravielli, Anthony. AN ADVENTURE IN GEOMETRY. New York: Viking Press, 1957.

Read, B.A. "Fibonacci Series in the Solar System." FIBONACCI QUARTERLY 8 (October 1970): 428-38.

RJV Financial Services. TRADING WITH FIBONACCI WAVE PROJECTIONS.

Runion, Garth E. THE GOLDEN SECTION AND RELATED CURIOSA. Glenview, IL: Scott Foresman & Co., 1972.

Sharp, W.E. "Fibonacci Drainage Patterns." FIBONACCI QUARTERLY 10 (December 1972): 643-55.

Sklarew, Arthur. TECHNIQUES OF A PROFESSIONAL COMMODITY CHART ANALYST. Pages 39-40, 42-44.

Smith, D.E. HISTORY OF MATHEMATICS. New York: Dover Publications, 1923.

Stevens, Peter S. PATTERNS IN NATURE. Boston: Little, Brown & Co., 1974.

Thompson, D'Arcy W. ON GROWTH AND FORM. Cambridge: Cambridge University Press, 1917.

Tompkins, Peter. SECRETS OF THE GREAT PYRAMID.

Vodopich, Don. TRADING FOR PROFITS WITH PRECISION TIMING.

Vorobev, N.N. FIBONACCI NUMBERS.

Williams, Larry. DEFINITIVE GUIDE TO FUTURES TRADING, Vol. 1. Pages 251-267.

Fibonacci Ratio Table

NUMERATOR → DENOMINATOR ↓	1	2	3	5	8	13	21	34	55	89	144
1	1.00	2.00	3.00	5.00	8.00	13.00	21.00	34.00	55.00	89.00	144.00
2	.50	1.00	1.50	2.50	4.00	6.50	10.50	17.00	27.50	44.50	72.00
3	.333	.667	1.00	1.667	2.667	4.33	7.00	11.33	18.33	29.67	48.00
5	.20	.40	.60	1.00	1.60	2.60	4.20	6.80	11.00	17.80	28.80
8	.125	.25	.375	.625	1.00	1.625	2.625	4.25	6.875	11.125	18.00
13	.077	.154	.231	.385	.615	1.00	1.615	2.615	4.23	6.846	11.077
21	.0476	.0952	.1429	.238	.381	.619	1.00	1.619	2.619	4.238	6.857
34	.0294	.0588	.0882	.147	.235	.3824	.6176	1.00	1.618	2.618	4.235
55	.01818	.03636	.0545	.0909	.1455	.236	.3818	.618	1.00	1.618	2.618
89	.011236	.02247	.0337	.0561	.08989	.146	.236	.382	.618	1.00	1.618
144	.006944	.013889	.0209	.0347	.05556	.0903	.1458	.236	.382	.618	1.00

Toward perfect ratios

987

Market Art!

Market-related art available through

Traders Press, Inc.®

**Varied selections of market-related
artwork and gifts are
available exclusively through
Traders Press, Inc.®
Currently available items are pictured on
our new website at
http://www.traderspress.com and in our Traders Catalog,
which is available
FREE upon request**

You can contact us at:
800-927-8222 ~ 864-298-0222
Fax 864-298-0221

**Traders Press, Inc.®
PO Box 6206
Greenville, SC 29606**

Serving Traders since 1975